"I've been trying to eat more vegans."

STORY
COLIN MITCHELL
BILL JEMAS
MICHAEL COAST

SCRIPT
COLIN MITCHELL

LAYOUTS
YOUNG HELLER
DAVID WILSON

PENCILS
YOUNG HELLER
DAVID WILSON

COLORS
TOMMASO MOSCARDINI
DINEI RIBEIRO

COVER
JOSE LUIS
CARLOS RENO

LETTERS
ELYSIA LIANG
CHARLOTTE GREENBAUM

EDITORS
ELYSIA LIANG
CHARLOTTE GREENBAUM

DOUBLE TAKE

RICHARD BROOKS | PRODUCTION ASSISTANT

MICHAEL COAST | STORY EDITOR

CLAIRE DRANGINIS | PRODUCTION COORDINATOR

CAROLINE FLANAGAN | PRODUCTION ASSISTANT

ALLISON GADSDEN | EDITORIAL INTERN

WILLIAM GRAVES | DIGITAL PRODUCTION ARTIST

CHARLOTTE GREENBAUM | EDITORIAL ASSISTANT

YOUNG HELLER | STORYBOARD ILLUSTRATOR

BILL JEMAS | GENERAL MANAGER

ELYSIA LIANG | EDITORIAL ASSISTANT

ROBERT MEYERS | MANAGING EDITOR

JULIAN ROWE | STORYBOARD ILLUSTRATOR

LILLIAN TAN | BUSINESS MANAGER

GABE YOCUM | SALES & MARKETING COORDINATOR

...emote #1. September 2015. Published by Double Take, LLC, a subsidiary of Take-Two Interactive Software, Inc. Office of publication: 38 ...7. 39 Street, 2nd Floor, New York, NY 10018. ©2015 Take-Two Interactive Software, Inc. All Rights Reserved. Printed in Canada.

1960's *Premiers*

	TV SHOWS	HIT MOVIES	TOP SINGLES
1960	The Flintstones The Andy Griffith Show My Three Sons	Spartacus Psycho Exodus	Theme from A Summer Place He'll Have to Go
1961	The Dick Van Dyke Show ABC's Wide World of Sports The Avengers	The Gun of Navarone West Side Story El Cid	Tossin' and Turnin I Fall to Pieces Michael
1962	The Jetsons The Beverly Hillbillies Tonight Show: Johnny Carson	Lawernce of Arabia The Longest Day In Search of the Castaways	Stranger on the Shore I Can't Stop Loving You Mashed Potato Time
1963	Doctor Who General Hospital Let's Make a Deal	Cleopatra How the West Was Won It's a Mad, Mad, Mad, Mad, World	Sugar Shack Surfin' U.S.A. The End of the World
1964	The Addams Family Gilligan's Island Jeopardy!	Mary Poppins Goldfinger My Fair Lady	I Want to Hold Your Hand She Loves You Hello, Dolly!
1965	I Dream of Jeannie Get Smart Hogan's Heroes	The Sound of Music Thunderball Dr. Zhivago	Wooly Bully I Can't Help Myself Satisfaction
1966	Batman Mission: Impossible Star Trek	The Bible: In the Beginning Hawaii Who's Afraid of Virginia Woolf	Ballad of the Green Berets Cherish Soul and Inspiration
1967	The Smothers Brothers The Newlywed Game The Prisoner	The Graduate The Jungle Book Doctor Dolittle	To Sir With Love The Letter Ode to Billie Joe
1968	Hawaii Five-O The Mod Squad 60 Minutes	Rosemary's Baby 2001: A Space Odyssey Planet of the Apes	Hey Jude Love is Blue Honey
1969	Sesame Street The Brady Bunch Monty Python's Flying Circus	Easy Rider Midnight Cowboy Butch Cassidy and the Sundance Kid	Sugar, Sugar Aquarius I Can't Get Next to You

Sunday, April 24, 1966, 10:15 pm
Evans County, Pennsylvania
KBRF
If you can make your way to one of the rescue stations, help will be waiting.

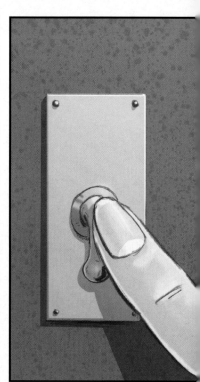

Yesterday, one white man and one Negro were killed.

Last August, Watts was the scene of the worst Negro rioting in the nation.

In Houston, surgeons placed an artificial heart in a man's chest.

The operation lasted six hours.

The patient survived, and the artificial pump worked.

Hello? Who's there? Hello, Kunkle, is that you?

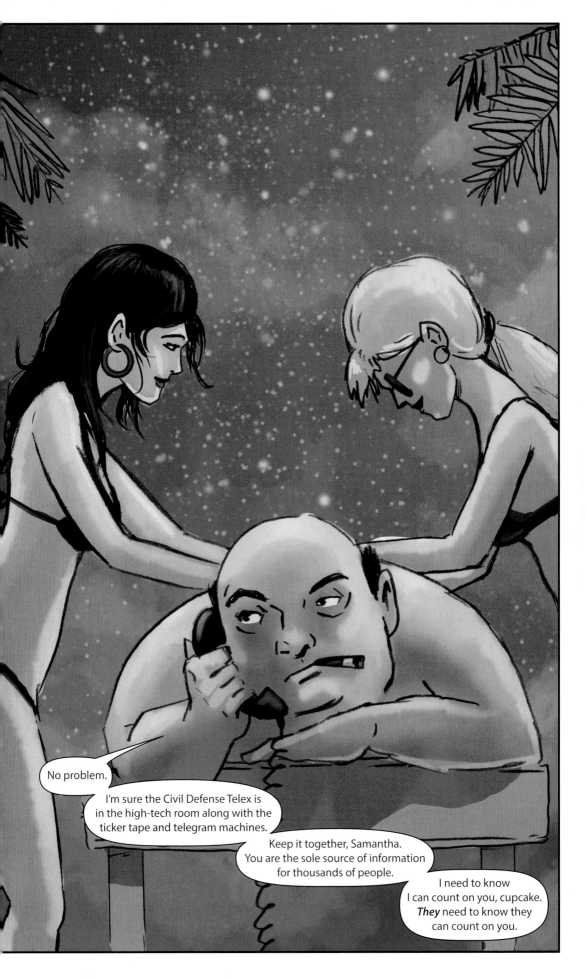

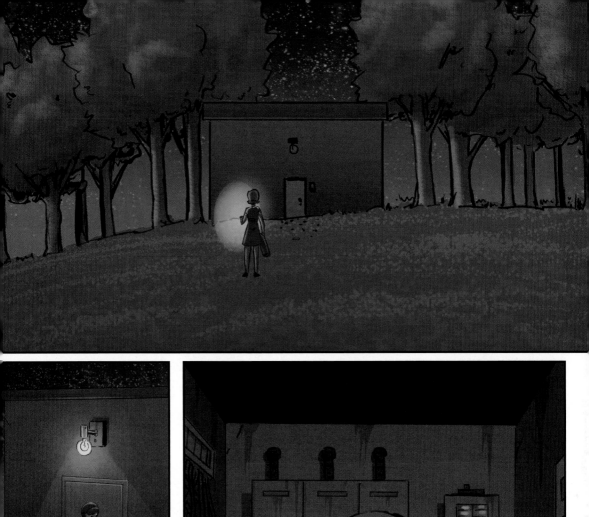
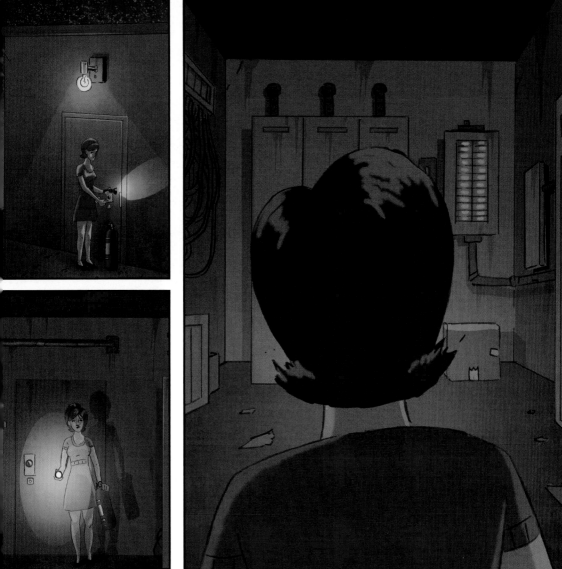

Can you survive the zombie apocalypse?

Yes? You probably think you can.

There is only one way to find out.

Play the **Dead Reign® RPG**. The core rule book, a few players, some dice and an active imagination are all you need to start playing. Rules are easy. Character creation is fast and fun. Combat, quick and deadly. Survival? Harder than you may think.

- **7 different types of zombies. Zombie combat and survival tips.**
- **6 Apocalyptic Character Classes and Ordinary People.**
- **101 Random Scenarios, Encounters, Settings and places of note.**
- **100 Random Corpse Searches, other tables, weapons & vehicles.**
- **Death Cults, their Priests, power over zombies and goals.**
- **Quick Roll Character Creation tables (10 minutes).**
- **5 sourcebooks provide more types of zombies, survival tips, new dangers and adventure.**
- **The Dead Reign™ core rule book is 224 pages – Cat. No. 230. A complete role-playing game book.**

Discover the Palladium Books® RPG Megaverse®

Fun to read. A blast to play. The Palladium role-playing rule system is the same in every game. This means once readers become familiar with one game, they can play them *ALL*.

Better yet, you can link and combine several game worlds to create epic, multi-dimensional adventures on a cosmic scale!

What's that? You've never seen a role-playing game? The role-playing core rule book contains all the rules and data you need to create characters and get you started. Each game or supplement is a magazine size soft-bound or hardcover book, 48-352 pages, and jam-packed with great art, heroes, villains, adventure and tons of ideas. **Dead Reign®** and **Robotech®** are excellent for those of you new to pen and paper RPG.

Rifts® is the Earth of the future, but a transformed and alien Earth where magic and technology coexist and realities from countless dimensions collide. Alien predators and supernatural monsters prey upon the human survivors and threaten to conquer the world.

Players can be any number of aliens, mutants, warriors, cyborgs, robots and wizards. Lines of magic crisscross the Earth, giving life to dragons, godlings and supernatural horrors. They also lead to dimensional gateways called "Rifts" that link the Earth to the infinite Megaverse®. In **Rifts®** anything is possible.

Unleash your imagination! Drop by our website, learn more about our games or make purchases from our online store. Also available in comic book and game stores everywhere.

www.palladiumbooks.com

Oh geez.
Ms. Prendergast?
I'm so sorry.

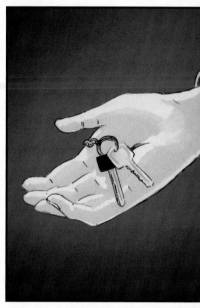

Braaaaiiiiins new packaging.

Same braaaaiiiiins taste.

ZOMBIE DICE

Don't get shotgunned.

SID MEIER'S CIVILIZATION®
BEYOND EARTH™

WWW.CIVILIZATION.COM

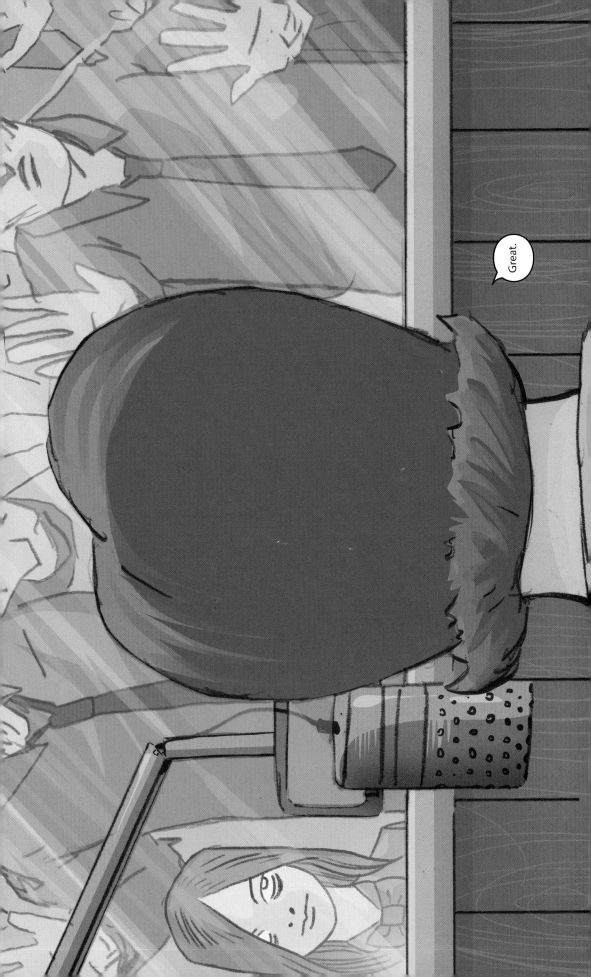

I had my plan that I would take Angie on a sunset picnic and then make out with her. Forceps.

I call her up and I tell her I've got a surprise for her and to meet me at the basketball courts.

She says she has a surprise for me and to come over to her place.

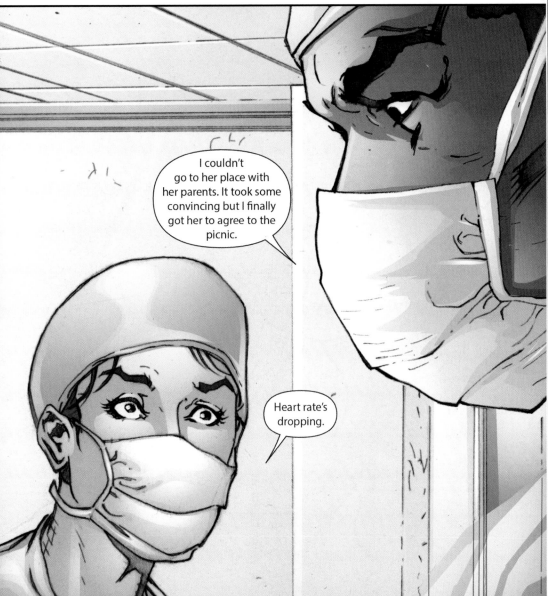

I couldn't go to her place with her parents. It took some convincing but I finally got her to agree to the picnic.

Heart rate's dropping.

PREVIEW: MEDIC #1

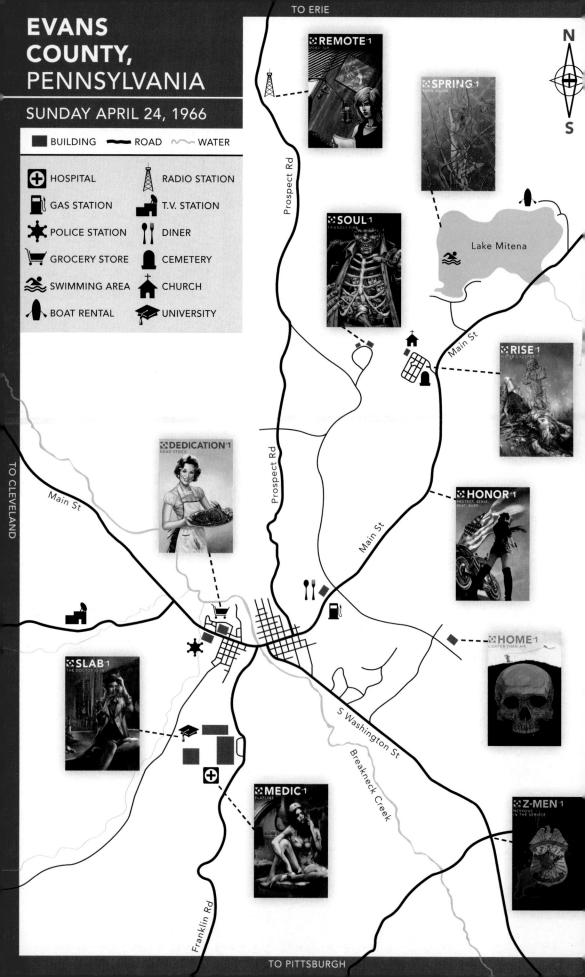